W9-BKI-647

What's New at the Zoo?

written by Judy Nayer
illustrated by Theresa Burns

 **McGraw-Hill School Division**

New York   Farmington

"What can we learn at the zoo?" asked Chuck.

"Let's see," said Hank. "Let's go together now!"

"Look! They swing from branch
to branch!" said Chuck.

"They swing a lot!" said Hank.

"Look!" said Hank. "They swim and swim in the tank!"

"They swim and jump a lot," said Chuck.

"Lunch!" said Hank. "They eat fish for lunch!"

"Let's go on this ride!" said Hank.

"What is in the grass?"

"Big, big cats!" said Chuck.

"The big cats run fast! It's fun to run fast," said Hank.

"Look, Hank!" said Chuck. "I can run fast, too!"